Snowie
the
Squareman

MICHELE SAVAUNAH ZIRKLE
Illustrated by JULIE SNEEDEN

Inside my boots, I hide my toes,
wiggle my mittens, scratch my nose.

Snow is falling on my head.

"Let's build a snowman," Grandpap said.

Roll the snow into a ball.

Roll and roll till down I fall.

Snow is cold down my neck.

Boomer the dog gives me a peck.

Grandpap blows
warm air
on my skin.
"Tummies have
heaters,"
he says
with a grin.

"Great for warming
you up in the snow.
Just cup your hands and
breathe out real slow."

Ball one all done. We are in luck.
Big like the tires on Daddy's truck.

Plop the belly on top. Hope it won't fall.
It's the size the full moon looks when you're small.

"Do snowmen have tummy heaters?" I say.
Grandpap laughs and says, "No way."

Next is his head.
No hair or beard.
Just an icy dome
that looks super weird.

Cucumber eyes and
a long, green bean nose.
I set his smile
with rocks in rows.

"I want to be different," Snowie says with a pout.

"Make me square at the bottom. I want to stand out!"

Grandpap shakes Snowie's
hand with his cane.

"Different is good," Grandpap says.

"Expands your brain."

Shovels shave square the round hump on the ground.

"Perfect," Snowie shouts
and we all dance around.

Grandpap, Snowie the Squareman and me
slurp hot chocolate under the tree.

Chocolate is warm in my tummy.
Snow is cold. Both are yummy!

Grandpaps are funny wherever they go.
Snowmen aren't all round, you know.

They can be square and just like you.

They can look different and be nice too.

Questions to Help Children Become Comfortable with Themselves

Are there ways you feel different from other kids or your friends?

What would your nose look like if you were a snowman?

How do you like to show you are different?

Do you feel okay/comfortable doing things differently than other people?

Ways to Express Diversity

- **How you spend time**
- **Foods you eat and dishes you eat on**
- **Hobbies and interests not necessarily taught in school**
- **How loudly or softly you speak**
- **How you show care for others**
- **Room decorations**
- **Clothing styles**
- **Hair color and styles**

ENJOY BUILDING YOUR OWN UNIQUE SNOWMAN OUTSIDE.

Draw Your Design Below!

About the Author

MICHELE SAVAUNAH ZIRKLE, MA, PhD, is a published author, holistic practitioner and transformation coach. Michele, a regular contributor to *The Journal of Health and Human Experience*, *Two-Lane Renaissance* and *Mindful Writer's Anthologies*, is best known for her inspirational stories and genre diversity. After twenty years of teaching high school English, she now teaches self-empowerment and healing to all ages in workshops and through her writing. When she isn't dancing a jig with her grandson, she is hiking in the woods or recording meditations. Wherever she is, you can bet she is story-telling and laughing as much as possible.

MicheleZirkle.com

About the Illustrator

Constantly inspired by the words and tales of imaginative authors, **JULIE SNEEDEN** uses color, light and creativity to bring her artwork into these magical worlds. To make the character of her images come to life, she draws upon a palette of tools including watercolor, pencil, charcoal, digital illustration, photography, and oil paints.

Julie studied Fine Arts in KwaZulu Natal, South Africa, but now lives with her family in the UK. Reading stories to her children has inspired her over the years to pursue the art of illustration. She has illustrated numerous stories to amazing authors all over the world.

Dedication

I dedicate this book to my two boys, Gabriel and Jacob, who inspire me every day to surround myself with love and enjoy each moment because time flies... and to my grandson, Kalmin, who can prod me into jumping on the trampoline way longer than I want to and whose smile is contagious. I wish his energy was too.

To every family member and friend who expressed genuine excitement about this project. I love each of you and am blessed that you not only accept my quirkiness but encourage me to be myself. Like Snowie who wants to stand out in the crowd, I can express my uniqueness and creativity with joy.

May you all find that joy and acceptance!

Year of the Book

135 Glen Avenue

Glen Rock, PA 17327

ISBN: 978-1-64649-297-8

Made in United States
Orlando, FL
16 August 2023